- Can you spot five hats hidden on these bookshelves?
- Turn to page 30 and see if you can find their owners.

This wildly word-tastic Wally Annual belongs to:

....

Published by Ladybird Books Ltd 2014
A Penguin Company
Penguin Books Ltd, 80 Strand, London, WC2R 0RL, UK
Penguin Books Australia Ltd, Camberwell, Victoria, Australia
Penguin Group (NZ), 67 Apollo Drive, Auckland, 0632, New Zealand
(a division of Pearson New Zealand Ltd)

Written by Mandy Archer
'The Five Powers of Woof' written by Kieran Grant and illustrated
by Pulsar Studio

ISBN: 978-0-72327-521-3

Printed in China

DID YOU KNOW?

1

Libraries the world over love Wally! Over sixty million Where's Wally? books* have been printed since the bobble-hatted rambler started his travels in 1987. Wally and Woof's adventures have been translated into a staggering thirty languages.

*Watch this Wally fact!
The number goes up all the time.

CONTENTS

Hey, Wally fans!

Welcome to my official 2015 Annual! Wizard Whitebeard has a shiny new copy in his library and now you have, too! This brilliant book is packed with puzzles and games, comics and crafts and stats and stories to astound and amaze you all year long.

All Wally fans love hunting and this annual doesn't disappoint! Flip to page 30 to discover a hide-and-seek game that is guaranteed to keep you poring over the pages for hours. Can you spot Woof, Wenda, Wizard Whitebeard, Odlaw and me hiding among the famous literary faces? It's all in the detail, folks, so keep an eye out for my lost key, Woof's bone, Wenda's camera and Odlaw's binoculars. As for Wizard Whitebeard's scroll — well, that could be anywhere!

The fun doesn't stop there — watch out for wacky goings-on, chuckle at tall tales and learn to draw my best pal, Woof. There's even a magical mystery to solve!

What are you waiting for? It's eyes down for a brand-new, bumper, bamboozling Wally treat!

Wally

DID YOU KNOW?

2

In August 2010, the tech team at Google tried to work out how many books have been published in modern history. The computer wizards used their most advanced algorithms to try to solve this seemingly impossible question. The answer came in as 129,864,880. Wowsers!

BEDLAM ON THE BOOKSHELVES

The Wizard has disappeared, but not without a trace. Use the back-to-front letter key to decipher Whitebeard's fridge-magnet message.

NB VMXSZMGVW HXILOO

_ _   _ _ _ _ _ _ _ _ _   _ _ _ _ _ _

YIRMTH LIWVI ZMW

_ _ _ _ _ _   _ _ _ _ _   _ _ _

VMORTSGVMNVMG. DSVM

_ _ _ _ _ _ _ _ _ _ _ _ _.   _ _ _ _

RG'H TLMV GSV LKKLHRGV

_ _'_   _ _ _ _   _ _ _   _ _ _ _ _ _ _ _

LXXFIH. XZM BLF SVOK,

_ _ _ _ _ _.   _ _ _   _ _ _   _ _ _ _,

DZOOB DZGXSVIH?

_ _ _ _ _   _ _ _ _ _ _ _ _?

A	B	C	D	E	F	G	H	I	J	K	L	M	N	O	P	Q	R	S	T	U	V	W	X	Y	Z
Z	Y	X	W	V	U	T	S	R	Q	P	O	N	M	L	K	J	I	H	G	F	E	D	C	B	A

Lost for words? The answer is on page 60.

Dear Reader,

Without the enchanted scroll, characters are clambering out of their books and the pages are getting madly muddled. Can you put this right? This annual will take you on a tour through Wizard Whitebeard's library. Look out for **ten characters (real or imagined)** along the way who are not where they should be. Write the name of each one into the Wizard's spell book on page 59. Spot all ten and you'll solve the mystery of the missing scroll!

WALLY TO THE RESCUE!

Wally and Woof are ready for adventure! The pair have pledged to lead the hunt for the Wizard's missing scroll. The path is sure to be strewn with dangerous encounters, crazy cliffhangers and red herrings.

But before Wally and Woof can start exploring, they must pack a few essentials. Every adventurer relies on the contents of his or her trusty kit bag! Study the picture for thirty seconds, then close the book. How many objects can you remember?

SWASHBUCKLING STORIES

The Adventure section is bristling with stories. Can you help Wally make it to the next page? Grab a pencil, then work your way through this pair of pulse-racing puzzles.

Classic Adventure Quiz

1 Which one of these characters is not a member of the Three Musketeers?

a. Aramis ☐
b. Richelieu ☐
c. D'Artagnan ☐

2 Which of these men is real and not a character from a classic adventure story?

a. Buffalo Bill ☐
b. Robinson Crusoe ☐
c. Tarzan ☐

3 Which of these authors penned *Treasure Island*?

a. Robert Louis Stevenson ☐
b. Jules Verne ☐
c. Michael Morpurgo ☐

4 What band of brothers does Peter Pan swear allegiance to?

a. The Brave Boys ☐
b. The Flying Boys ☐
c. The Lost Boys ☐

5 What is the first name of modern adventure writer A. Horowitz?

a. Aubrey ☐
b. Anthony ☐
c. Arthur ☐

6 What animal is Buck, the hero of Jack London's *Call Of The Wild*?

a. A bear ☐
b. A chimp ☐
c. A dog ☐

Fearsome Feats

Sometimes truth is stranger than fiction! Draw a line to match each real-life adventurer to their most famous achievement.

1. **Jacques Cousteau**

2. **Neil Armstrong**

3. **Roald Amundsen**

4. **Sir Ranulph Fiennes**

5. **Amelia Earheart**

6. **Sir Edmund Hillary**

A. Tenzing Norgay's climbing partner on the first successful expedition to the peak of Mount Everest.

B. An undersea scientist and marine researcher who helped to develop the Aqua-Lung.

C. Active adventurer widely claimed to be the world's greatest living explorer.

D. An American astronaut and the first person to walk on the surface of the Moon.

E. The first explorer to reach the North Pole.

F. The first female aviator to fly solo across the Atlantic Ocean.

GREAT LIVES

Well, well . . . look who's turned up in the Biography section! It's time to read up on some of your favourite famous faces.

Wally

Our happy-go-lucky hero is a storybook classic, recognized all over the world! Wally roams far and wide, but he never steps out without his red and white stripy sweater and distinctive bobble hat. Wally and his walking stick have adventured in some unbelievable places - from the sparkle-topped towers of Fairyland to the eye-popping World of Wallys.

Favourite book: Wally's very own travel journal always makes fascinating reading!

Wenda

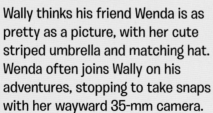

Wally thinks his friend Wenda is as pretty as a picture, with her cute striped umbrella and matching hat. Wenda often joins Wally on his adventures, stopping to take snaps with her wayward 35-mm camera.

Favourite book: **Photography for Beginners**.

Odlaw

There's no two ways about it - Odlaw can't resist mixing up mischief, bringing on bedlam and stirring up trouble! The rotter is always on Wally's trail, looming out of shadowy corners and leaping up from behind bushes. If you see a flash of black and yellow, beware - Odlaw is up to something once again!

Favourite book: **The Strange Case of Dr Jekyll and Mr Hyde** by Robert Louis Stevenson.

Woof

He can be tricky to spot, but, rest assured, wherever Wally is, Woof will never be far behind! After a hard day's ramble, Woof likes nothing better than curling up with his bone and a howlingly funny comic.

Favourite book: Woof was brought up on **The Hound of the Baskervilles**, but now he's crazy for cartoon capers.

Wizard Whitebeard

Wizard Whitebeard often joins Wally on his travels. The legendary magician carries a striped staff that is said to have ancient powers. Whitebeard has been around so long, he's read most of the books in print and plenty that are out of print, too. He's as wise as wise could be, but Wizard Whitebeard always seems to end up losing his magical scroll!

Favourite book: The Wizard scours every page of his daily newspaper - it's the only thing that he hasn't already read!

The Wally Watchers

Wally's loyal line of Watchers have followed him through thick and thin. They're a dogged and enthusiastic bunch who don't get put off easily. They all know Wally's journeys will lead them to spectacular sights, exciting experiences and awesome adventures. Fitting the whole stripy-garbed crew into Wizard Whitebeard's library is a mighty squeeze, but they don't mind a bit.

Favourite book: The **Complete Encyclopedia Britannica** - with many volumes, the Wally Watchers can all read it at the same time!

The Five Powers of Woof!

AT WALLY'S HOUSE - WALLY AND WENDA ARE HEADED OUT OF THE FRONT DOOR, ALL KITTED UP FOR AN ADVENTURE.

COME ON, WENDA. WIZARD WHITEBEARD IS WAITING FOR US IN THE LAND OF FLYING CARPETS!

WOOF, I NEED YOU TO STAY HERE AND GUARD THE HOUSE.

30 SECONDS LATER...

ZZZZZZZZZZ...

...ZZZZZZZZZZZZ - HUH??

I'M A SUPERHERO! I CAN FLY!

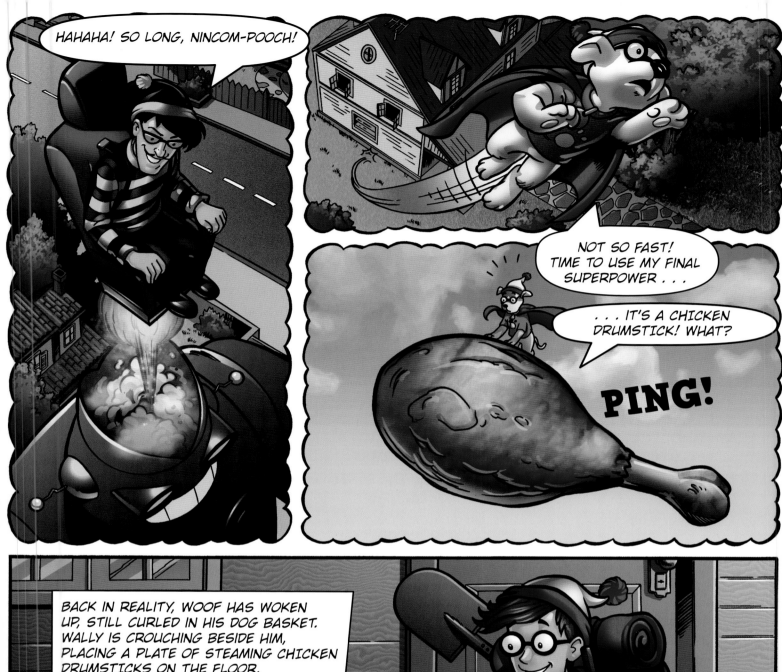

MAKE YOUR OWN
ILLUMINATED LETTER

Wally has discovered piles and piles of decorated parchments in a dusty corner of Wizard Whitebeard's library. Before printed books came along, people used to write stories by hand, using quills made from feathers.

After the story had been written, an artist would decorate each page. These decorations were called illuminations, because they filled the manuscript with light.

An illuminated letter is the large, decorated letter used to start a new page or chapter.

Wally has had a go at illuminating the first letter of his name, with spectacular results! Why don't you try, too?

Illuminated manuscripts

The Book of Kells

This lavish masterpiece is one of Ireland's greatest treasures and is believed to date back to the 800s.

1. Tape a sheet of parchment paper on to a sturdy piece of cardboard. This will help the paper stay flat while you work.

2. Find a pencil, choose a letter to illuminate and lightly draw its outline on to the parchment. Now use a ruler to draw a border around the letter to keep your artwork contained.

3. It's time to get creative! Fill the inside of your letter with a design that represents you. You might want to draw your favourite things, hobbies, pets or a pattern that you like. You could even design a unique coat of arms or add extra pictures round the edges.

4. Use colouring pencils or paint to fill the letter with colour. Leave it to dry if necessary.

5. Take a gold or silver pen and carefully highlight elements of the letter to make the design even richer. When you have finished, outline the details with a thin black marker pen, then rub out any pencil marks that can still be seen.

6. Carefully peel away the masking tape. Dab the back of the parchment with PVA glue and then mount it on to a sheet of coloured card.

You will need:
- Heavy white parchment paper
- A piece of strong cardboard
- Masking tape
- Scissors
- Pencil
- Ruler
- Colouring pencils or watercolour paints and a paintbrush
- Gold or silver calligraphy pen
- Thin black marker pen
- Rubber
- PVA glue
- Large sheet of coloured card

Is your illumination utterly inspirational? Why not use it to start off a brand-new story or poem starring . . . you!

LET'S DETECT!

Woof barks when Wally steps past the Crime shelves. The hound has sniffed out a clue to the Case of the Missing Scroll! Detective Wally rummages in his rucksack and pulls out a magnifying glass. Are you ready, Wally Watchers? You'll need to be extra observant to investigate the scene of this crime!

Crime scenes must be treated with care. Super sleuths know that even the most careful criminals always leave something behind. Peer through Wally's magnifying glass, then tick the correct label for each find.

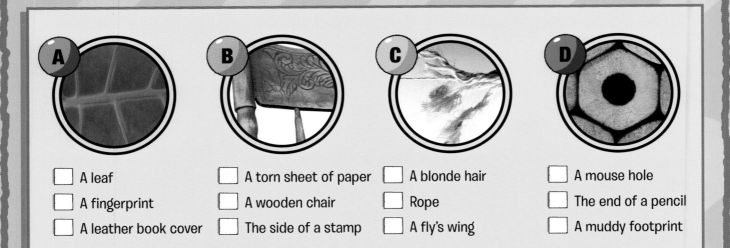

A
- [ ] A leaf
- [ ] A fingerprint
- [ ] A leather book cover

B
- [ ] A torn sheet of paper
- [ ] A wooden chair
- [ ] The side of a stamp

C
- [ ] A blonde hair
- [ ] Rope
- [ ] A fly's wing

D
- [ ] A mouse hole
- [ ] The end of a pencil
- [ ] A muddy footprint

Excellent evidence

Criminal experts use all sorts of advanced technology to convict suspects, but fingerprint testing is still one of the most effective examples of forensic science. Although we can't always spot them, the oil and water on our hands leaves a fingerprint mark whenever we touch something. Everybody's fingerprints are unique – even those belonging to identical twins!

Why not get to know your fingerprints a little better? All you need is a balloon and an ink pad. Put one finger in the ink pad, then carefully press it on to the side of the balloon. When the ink is dry, blow your balloon up – now your fingerprint will be large enough for you to study every loop, ridge and arch!

NOT SO HAPPY ENDINGS ...

Wandering through the library shelves, Wally has been inspired to star in his own fairy tale. All he needs now is a writer. Yes Wally Watchers, Wally needs YOU!

Are you ready to weave a riveting yarn, set in a magical kingdom, far far away? You've got the fairy-tale ingredients, now all you need is a pen, some friends and your imagination!

To start, one person writes a line, then folds the paper to cover the writing, and passes it on to the next person, who writes another line underneath. When the piece of paper gets to the last person, they write the ending. To discover whether Wally lives happily ever after, simply unfold your story and find out! Use the ingredients lists to start your story off!

Fairy-tale Ingredients

Terrifying twists and turns
What if Wally . . .
- ate a poisoned apple?
- slept for a hundred years?
- pricked his finger?

Spectacular settings
- a royal palace
- a deep, dark forest
- a spiralling beanstalk

Magical beings
- wizards
- mermaids
- dwarves

Vile villains
- a wicked queen
- a fire-breathing dragon
- a scheming baron

Awesome animals
- bridge-tripping billy goats
- an ugly duckling
- house-building piggies

Gracious goodies
- a gallant prince
- a sleeping princess
- an innocent brother and sister

Mother Goose's
MAGICAL MAZE

A gaggle of old friends are waiting for Wally in the Fairy-tales section! Would you care for a walk through Fairyland?

Start

Use a pencil to trace a path for Wally and Woof. You'll need to be wide-eyed and wary if you don't want to come to a grim end. There are wolves in the forest, trolls under bridge and peril looming at each twist and turn.

DID YOU KNOW?

4

Fairy tales are shared in countries all around the world. Most are hundreds of years old, and have been passed down through songs and stories. Every adventure shimmers with magic – from terrifying trolls and demon dragons to fairy godmothers and frog princes.

Finish

THE REAL LIFE
HISTORY OF BOOKS

One thing's for sure, books have been around for a long time. From cave paintings to the Internet, we communicate and share ideas – whatever they may be! Join Wally on a whistle-stop tour through the history of books . . .

3,300 BCE — Clay tablets are used in Mesopotamia.

c.2,500 BCE — The earliest known papyrus scrolls are created in ancient Egypt.

c.350 BCE — Scribes in China start to write on pieces of silk.

100 — Paper, made from tree bark, is invented in China.

868 — The earliest surviving piece of woodblock printing is made in China. Scrolls are folded like a concertina and then bound along one edge.

1200s — Paper mills are established in Italy and beyond.

1476 — William Caxton sets up a printing press in Westminster, London.

1605 — The first newspaper is circulated in Strasbourg, France.

1753 — The British Museum's department of books is opened. This eventually becomes the British Library.

1830 — William Austin Burt invents an early typewriter, calling it 'the typographer'.

1841 — The first paperback books are published by Tauchnitz.

1960s — Early e-books are published.

1987 — The first *Where's Wally?* title is released.

2014 — Wally's new annual appears on a bookshelf near you!

DID YOU KNOW?

Over the years, William Burt's typographer evolved into a mass-produced computer with a QWERTY keyboard. This all ended with the digital age. The last ever typewriter made in the UK was created on 20th November 2012 by Brother. It was donated to the Science Museum in London.

QUIRKY KINGS and CRAFTY QUEENS QUIZ

How much do you know about the merry (and not-so-merry) kings and queens of England?

Work your way through this quiz. Will you earn yourself a knighthood or land yourself a trip to the Tower? When you've finished, tally up your score, using the answers on page 60 – your fate awaits at the bottom of the page.

1 Which king hid in an oak tree after the battle of Worcester?
a. George IV ☐
b. Charles II ☐
c. William II ☐

2 Which monarch established the Union Jack flag?
a. James I ☐
b. Elizabeth I ☐
c. Richard I ☐

3 Henry VIII famously had six wives. What was the name of the last one?
a. Catherine of Aragon ☐
b. Catherine Parr ☐
c. Anne Boleyn ☐

4 Who is the longest serving monarch in British history?
a. Victoria ☐
b. George III ☐
c. Elizabeth II ☐

5 Which unfortunate relatives of Richard III was he said to have murdered in the Tower of London?
a. His sisters ☐
b. His parents ☐
c. His nephews ☐

6 Which king earned himself the name of 'Lionheart'?
a. Richard I ☐
b. Richard II ☐
c. Richard III ☐

7 Which king or queen established Buckingham Palace as a royal residence?
a. Mary I ☐
b. Anne ☐
c. George III ☐

8 King Harold II met his end at the Battle of Hastings in 1066. How is he believed to have died?
a. Stabbed with a knife ☐
b. Shot through the eye with an arrow ☐
c. Trampled by a stampeding horse ☐

9 How many times did Elizabeth I get married?
a. Once ☐
b. Twice ☐
c. She never got married ☐

10 Who is second in line to Elizabeth II's throne?
a. Prince Charles ☐
b. Prince William ☐
c. Prince Andrew ☐

How did you do?

7-10 Arise, Sir Wally! An expert like you would be at home in any royal court.

4-6 A promising start, but your princely facts are still foggy. Time to flick through a history book!

0-3 You may be a loyal subject, but your kingly know-how is paltry in the extreme. Off with your head!

CREATURE CONSEQUENCES

Wally can't help but shudder as he steps past the Wizard's eye-boggling collection of magic books. These leather-bound volumes have come to life, too! Werewolves, ogres and serpents writhe and roar from every page.

Can you come up with a new monster to protect Wally on his quest?

You will need:
At least 2 players
Sheets of blank paper
Coloured pencils

How to play:

1. Take a sheet of paper each and a pencil. Carefully fold your piece of paper like a concertina into four sections. Unfold the paper again and smooth it out.

2. When everybody is ready, draw a beast's head in the top section of the paper, taking care that no one can see you. Make the drawing as dramatic and fantastical as you like.

3. Fold the top section of the paper back down, making sure that only a small section of the creature's neck can be seen. Ask everyone to pass their sheets of paper to the person on their left.

4. On the second section of the paper, secretly draw a monster chest, tummy and arms. This could be in the same style as the head you drew, or it could look completely different! When you've finished, fold the section over again and pass it on.

5. On the next sheet of paper, draw a pair of monster legs in the third section. Again, when you're finished fold it back up and pass it along to the next player.

6. The bottom section of the next sheet should have just enough space for a pair of monster feet. Draw these in, then close the paper up and pass it round one last time.

Make your monster as mad as you can. Why not add feathers, fangs, horns or a row of prickly spines?

The big reveal . . .

When your monsters are finished, take turns to unfold the sheets of paper and discover the results! Each of the monsters will be a brilliantly bonkers mismatch of weird and wonderful body parts. Colour your monsters in and then give them each a name.

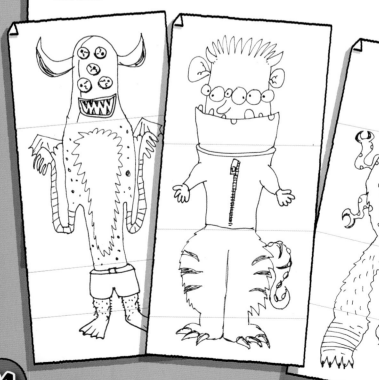

BLOODCURDLING BEASTS AND FEARSOME FIENDS

Which monsters do you most dread finding under the bed? Watch out, these gruesome creatures have been let loose in the library!

Frankenstein's Monster
***Frankenstein* by Mary Shelley**
Victor Frankenstein builds his monster in a laboratory, but is horrified when the creature leaps up and runs off into the night.

The Giant Squid
***Twenty Thousand Leagues Under The Sea* by Jules Verne**
This hulking octopus-like beast lurks below the waves, ready and waiting to devour sailors.

Cyclops
***The Odyssey* by Homer**
A classical monster that dates all the way back to ancient Greece. Cyclops is a man-eating giant with a single, unblinking eye.

Dracula
***Dracula* by Bram Stoker**
Count Dracula is the original vampire – a Transylvanian bloodsucker who roams at night searching for human victims.

WIZARD MEMORY TRICKS

Wally has bumped into Wizard Whitebeard! The worried wiz is scouring the shelves in the Memoirs section for his missing scroll.

Wally wonders if the enchanted scroll has been swiped or if Whitebeard has just forgotten where he put it. The wily wizard snorts – he never forgets anything! He can recall every book in the library and what's inside it, too.

Magical mnemonics

How does the wizard have such a marvellous memory? It's all down to mnemonics. Mnemonics are funny tricks that help you remember things. It could be a little rhyme that sticks in your head or a series of initials listing the order of something important.

Here's a common memory rhyme that you might have already heard:

**Thirty days has September,
April, June and November;
All the rest have thirty-one,
Excepting February alone:
Which has but twenty-eight in fine,
Til leap year gives it twenty-nine.**

How about these? Each one has been devised to help with spelling headaches:

NECESSARY
Not **E**very **C**at **E**ats **S**ardines (**S**ome **A**re **R**eally **Y**ummy)

RHYTHM
Rhythm **H**elps **Y**our **T**wo **H**ips **M**ove

Quick quiz

What do these mnemonics help you remember? Each of these phrases represents a collection of related words or names. Study the sets of initials, then use the clues to crack each one.

RICHARD OF YORK GAVE BATTLE IN VAIN

Clue: It ends in a crock of gold.

EVERY GOOD BOY DESERVES FRUIT

Clue: Say it or sing it?

WHO SAID THAT?

Here are six of Wally's favourite phrases. Can you work out who said what? Read the great quotations and then draw a line to match the saying to the correct character and book.

1. 'There is nothing – absolutely nothing – half so much worth doing as simply messing about in boats.'

2. 'I am the wisest man alive, for I know one thing, and that is that I know nothing.'

3. 'I'm not a dwarf! I'm a girl. And actually, I'm the tallest in my class.'

4. 'Bah, humbug!'

5. 'To be, or not to be, that is the question . . .'

6. 'Whizzpopping is a sign of happiness. It is music in our ears! You surely is not telling me that a *little* whizzpopping is forbidden among human beans?'

A. Lucy Pevensie, *The Lion, the Witch and the Wardrobe*, by C. S. Lewis

B. Hamlet, *Hamlet* by William Shakespeare

C. The BFG, *The BFG* by Roald Dahl

D. Ebenezer Scrooge, *A Christmas Carol* by Charles Dickens

E. *The Republic* by Plato

F. Ratty, *The Wind in the Willows* by Grahame Green

Five of these sayings were uttered by fictional characters, but one is credited to a real person. Which is it?

DID YOU KNOW?

6

Not everybody wants their words be read by other people! Samuel Pepys started a diary in 1660. His journal recounts two momentous events in vivid detail - the devastating Plague in 1665 and the Great Fire of London in 1666. Pepys kept his diary secret and deliberately wrote in shorthand so no one else could read it.

EXTINCT!

What do Tasmanian tigers and great auks have in common? They are all amazing animal species that have sadly died out forever. Field notes and drawings are our last record of the extinct creatures that used to roam Earth.

Use this space to draw a picture of an extinct animal species - real or imagined. Will you sketch a dinosaur or a dodo? You could even create a strange hybrid creature, like the half-zebra half-horse quagga that was last seen in the 1880s.

Name .... Sketched by ....

Reason for extinction ....

DID YOU KNOW? 7

Charles Darwin was one of the most brilliant Victorian naturalists. His great work *The Origin of the Species* totally changed the way that scientists thought about survival and evolution.

ScHoOL SPoT!

Nature is all around us, even in busy cities. It's never too late to start studying and protecting the natural world. Wally and Woof have a challenge for you – how many different plants and animals can you spot on your way to school? Grab a notebook and transform yourself into a nature detective!

Take note!

Create your own field diary, jotting down lists and descriptions of everything that you find. Add drawings to bring your discoveries to life or go on a mini photo safari!

Hedge hunting

Start your hunt by peering into any hedges that you pass. Hedges are the natural habitat for over 24,000 species of bugs alone! Larger animals also use them as corridors, and they often leave tracks behind them. Look out for prints on the ground, stray feathers or pieces of fur caught on branches.

Tree of life

Trees are beautiful to look at, but they also support lots of other life. Look for creeping caterpillars, nesting birds and squirrels leaping from branch to branch.

Look down

Tread carefully: the ground is littered with animal evidence!

Add your own nature spots here . . .

Do not disturb

All budding naturalists must protect their local habitat. If you touch anything, take care to handle it gently and then return it to where you found it. Never pick flowers or plants, or take animals away from their homes.

On your way to school can you spot a . . .?

- [ ] Bee
- [ ] Beetle
- [ ] Blackbird
- [ ] Centipede
- [ ] Dragonfly
- [ ] Earthworm
- [ ] Fox
- [ ] Frog
- [ ] Ladybird
- [ ] Magpie
- [ ] Millipede
- [ ] Mole
- [ ] Moth
- [ ] Mouse
- [ ] Newt
- [ ] Pigeon
- [ ] Rabbit
- [ ] Red Admiral butterfly
- [ ] Robin
- [ ] Snail
- [ ] Sparrow
- [ ] Spider
- [ ] Squirrel
- [ ] Starling
- [ ] Vole
- [ ] Woodlouse

LOST IN THE LIBRARY!

LIBRARY LOGBOOK

Without the enchanted scroll Wizard Whitebeard's books are in complete disarray! Can you spot all the following things in the library?

 Wally

 Wenda

 Woof's tail

 Wizard Whitebeard

 Odlaw

 The enchanted scroll

 Wally's lost key

 Woof's bone

 Wenda's camera

 Odlaw's binoculars

 Alice

 Guy Fawkes

 Hamlet

 Oliver Twist

 Sherlock Holmes

 Peter Pan

 Frankenstein's Monster

 Cinderella

 Florence Nightingale

 Humpty Dumpty

 Cyclops

 Dracula

 Samuel Pepys

 A dish and a spoon

 Little Bo Peep

 A gingerbread man

 Robin Hood

 Mr Tumnus

 Three bowls of porridge

 A cow jumping over the Moon

 Tweedledum and Tweedledee

 A giraffe

 Rapunzel

 Abraham Lincoln

 D'Artagnan

 Neptune

The Invisible Man

The Giant Squid

Charles Darwin

Pinocchio

A caveman

Plato

The Man in the Iron Mask

The Cheshire Cat

Sir Edmund Hillary

Three Little Pigs

The Big Bad Wolf

Queen of Hearts

The Owl and the Pussycat

The Frog Prince

Jack and his beanstalk

A Lion, a Witch and a Wardrobe

Robinson Crusoe

A mermaid

William Shakespeare

Santa Claus

Boudicca

Buffalo Bill

Admiral Nelson

Jacques Cousteau

Amelia Earhart

A mummy

A boxer

The Tinman

A robot

Captain Hook

Rip Van Winkle

A superhero

A ballet dancer

A rugby player

A knight

A soldier

A snake charmer

Francis Drake

Don Quixote

A frogman

A witch

A bear

A Roman standard-bearer

A druid

READ ALL ABOUT IT!

Wally wanders into the Newspapers section just as the latest issue of the *Traveller's Times* lands on the reading desk! Wizard Whitebeard's missing scroll makes front page news, but what light can the paper shed on the mystery?

Congratulations! You've been appointed the editor-at-large of the *Traveller's Times* with immediate effect! This edition is in your hands. Grab a pencil and finish the jaw-dropping front cover. Think up the headline, draw in the pictures and complete the article. Make it sensational!

25p

2014 Edition

THE TRAVELLER'S TIMES

Cover story by roving staff reporter,

....

Wizard Whitebeard's library was at the centre of a controversy last night, when reports emerged that it had been the scene of a curious crime.

A gathering crowd of Wally Watchers claimed that an enchanted scroll had been stolen from the Wizard's secret bookshelf. The culprit was nowhere to be seen.

Fantastic theories and surreal speculations are already beginning to circulate about the thief. In the meantime, the library is in turmoil.

With exclusive photos by Wenda.

'Not only is the scroll priceless,' claimed one staggered bystander, 'it has rare and magical properties.'

Rare indeed. Witnesses have already reported unusual activities at the library. Since the scroll incident, books are said to be opening by themselves, while unusual characters allegedly roam the aisles. Strange sightings include Humpty Dumpty sat on a shelf, Alice stepping into a mirror and

....

....

....

....

....

....

....

Can storybook characters really be at large in the library? How will they all get on? What will happen if they manage to get out? The prospect of Count Dracula, Captain Hook or the Snow Queen being unleashed is a tremble-inducing prospect. The world waits with trepidation to discover how the story will unfold!

Just as the Wizard's predicament was looking utterly troublesome, Wally arrived on the scene. Our heroic rambler has offered to pitch in and lead the search for the magical parchment.

'The Wizard's scroll has a habit of going astray,' said Wally cheerfully, 'but I'm quietly confident Woof and I will sniff it out again.'

In an exclusive interview for the *Traveller's Times*, Wally agreed to share his theory about the scroll's whereabouts.

'It's a magical mystery, all right,' he began.

....

....

....

....

....

....

....

....

....

....

....

TRAVELLER'S TIMES EXCLUSIVE

DID YOU KNOW?

8

In Great Britain about 12 million newspapers are bought every single day, with another 3 million free papers being picked up and read. The oldest surviving English newspaper is called *Berrow's Worcester Journal*. The paper started publishing regularly in 1709!

HOW TO DRAW
WOOF

Wally always enjoys a good read in the Pets section – there are ferret facts, ideas for iguanas and tons of tips for terrapins. Woof has tracked down something even more interesting, however – a guide to drawing puppy portraits!

Find a pencil and copy the pictures in order. You'll be surprised how a few simple circles and lines can combine to create a pawfectly persuasive Woof portrait! When you're finished, colour Woof's red and white striped hat.

① ② ③

④ ⑤ ⑥ ⑦

T. S. Eliot 'When You're a Grown-up' by Michael Rosen and 'The Dentist and the Crocodile' by Roald Dahl. **39**

WEIRD SCIENCE

CRAZY HOME EXPERIMENTS

Test tubes bubble, machines clank and Bunsen burners flare in the Weird Science section. Wally and Woof are treated to some staggering sights – floating eggs, exploding fizz and balloons that won't pop! The science here is weird, wacky and head-scratchingly simple. Are you ready to have a go? You don't need a lab. Every one of these testing tricks can be tried out in the comfort of your own home!

The unpoppable balloon

You will need:

- A latex balloon
- A wooden kebab skewer
- A small pot of cooking oil

1. Blow up the balloon until it's nearly full of air. Hold the end and slowly let about a third of the air escape. Tie a knot in the end.

2. Take the skewer and dip the end into the cooking oil until it's fully coated.

3. Hold the balloon in one hand and carefully insert the skewer at the bottom of the balloon where the latex doesn't appear so stretched. Keep on pushing!

What happens:

The skewer will go into the balloon and out the other side!

Why?

Pushing the skewer through the end of the balloon means that it enters the latex at the point of least stress, allowing the molecules inside to stretch without breaking.

The magical floating egg

You will need:

- An egg
- Water
- a spoon
- a glass
- 6 tablespoons table salt

1. Pour water into the glass and until it is half full.

2. Spoon in around six tablespoons of salt and give it a good stir.

3. Carefully pour in enough water to fill the glass up, keeping the glass very still.

4. Gently lower the egg into the water.

What happens:

The egg should float mysteriously in the middle of the glass.

Why?

Water with salt in it is denser than plain cold water. The egg, therefore, drops through the water in the top half of the glass until it reaches the denser, saltier liquid below.

The exploding drink bottle

You will need:

- A large bottle of diet cola
- A thin funnel
- Half a packet of mint Mentos™

1. Stand the cola bottle in the middle of an open space and slowly undo the lid.

2. Put a funnel into the top of the cola and very quickly drop the mints into the bottle.

3. Take cover!

What happens:

A towering eruption of diet cola should burst out of the bottle!

Why?

Scientists are still trying to thrash this out, but the cola eruption is believed to be caused by the carbon dioxide in the drink combining with the little bumps on the surface of the mints.

WHERE'S WALLY? WARNING

This experiment is messy, so ask an adult's permission first and only do it outside!

Bendy water

You will need:

- A plastic comb

1. Turn on a tap so that it is running very gently.

2. Take the comb and pass it through your hair at least a dozen times.

3. Move the comb towards the water, but do not let it touch it.

What happens:

The stream of water will magically bend towards the comb.

Why?

When you comb your hair you create static electricity, giving the comb a negative charge. When you move it towards the water, this negative charge pushes away the negative charge in the liquid, leaving a positive charge. The negative and positive charges are attracted to each other, pulling the water towards the comb.

'S' Spells SOLUTION

Wizard Whitebeard is consulting his spell book in a desperate bid to put things right. The ancient sage has happened upon an incantation that will reveal the scroll thief. If it didn't have so many missing words, he'd be able to shake his staff and shout it out loud!

You and Wally have turned up at just the right moment. Can you fill in the blanks and unmask the mischief-maker? The solution is hiding in the red vertical column of this word grid. Before you can even start to complete it, you'll need to fill the blanks in the clue list first (right).

Every clue features the name of a character who has popped up on a page in the annual where they don't belong. Search for each imposter, then write their names into the right clue. The page numbers at the end of each line will help you work out where to look.

When your clues are cracked, you can start completing the word square. Good luck, Wally Watchers!

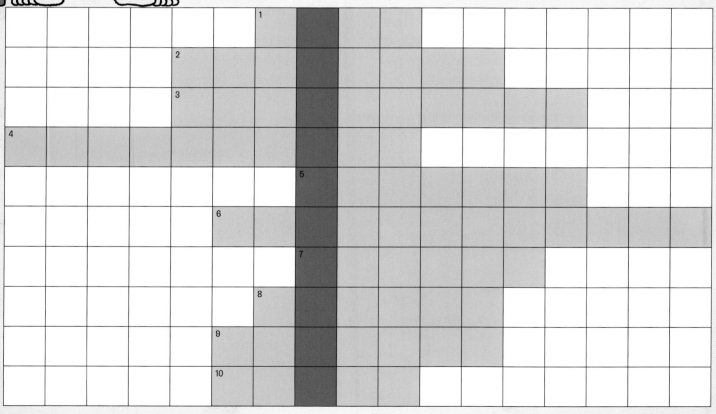

Clues

1. The golden inside of _ _ _ _ _ _ _ _ _ _ _. (Pages 10-11)

2. The brave patients of _ _ _ _ _ _ _ _ _ _ _ _ _ _ _ _ _ _ _ _ _. (Pages 16-17)

3. The houses that treasonous _ _ _ _ _ _ _ _ _ had in his sights. (Pages 20-21)

4. The curious place that _ _ _ _ _ discovers down a rabbit hole. (Pages 24-25)

5. The first name of the playwright that penned the tragic tale of _ _ _ _ _ _. (Pages 28-29)

6. The doctor who built the terrible _ _ _ _ _ _ _ with a bolt through its neck. (Pages 36-37).

7. The one thing that _ _ _ _ _ _ _ _ doesn't want to do. (Pages 40-41)

8. _ _ _ _ _ _ _ _ _ _ _ _ _ _ _'s very loyal assistant. (Pages 38-39)

9. The elegant glass object that fits _ _ _ _ _ _ _ _ _ _ a treat. (Pages 50-51)

10. A true friend to poor little _ _ _ _ _ _ _ _ _ _ _. (Pages 56-57)

It's ....

Draw the rascal's
mug shot in here.

Congratulations! Now the source of the spellbinding situation is
revealed, Wizard Whitebeard's enchanted scroll can be returned!

ANSWERS

Page 7 Bedlam on the Bookshelves

MY ENCHANTED SCROLL BRINGS ORDER AND ENLIGHTENMENT. WHEN IT'S GONE THE OPPOSITE OCCURS. CAN YOU HELP, WALLY WATCHERS?

Page 10 Classic Adventure Quiz

1. b. Richelieu
2. a. Buffalo Bill
3. a. Robert Louis Stevenson
4. c. The Lost Boys
5. b. Anthony
6. c. A dog

Fearsome Feats

1. B
2. D
3. E
4. C
5. F
6. A

Page 18 Let's Detect!

A. A leaf
B. A wooden chair
C. Rope
D. The end of a pencil

Pages 20-21 Mother Goose's Magical Maze

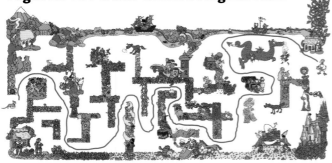

Page 25 Quirky Kings and Crafty Queens Quiz

1. b. Charles II
2. a. James I
3. b. Catherine Parr
4. a. Victoria
5. c. His nephews
6. a. Richard I
7. c. George III
8. b. Shot through the eye with an arrow
9. c. She never got married
10. b. Prince William

Pages 28 Wizard Memory Tricks

Quick quiz

The colours of the rainbow: red, orange, yellow, green, blue, indigo and violet.

The order of musical notes crossing the lines on the treble clef: E, G, B, D, F.

Page 27 Who Said That?

1. F
2. E
3. A
4. D
5. B
6. C

Plato is the only real person in the list.

Pages 40-41

Wally's Wordsearch

B	I	N	O	C	U	L	A	R	S		
		R	O	L	L	M	A	T			
	L			S	P	A	D	E			R
	I					I					U
	C	E		A			O				C
	N	L			R						K
	E	T				E					S
	P	T					M				A
		E		T	E	L	L	A	M	C	
W	A	L	K	I	N	G	S	T	I	C	K

Loopy Literature

1. Hamlet
2. Humpty Dumpty
3. Oliver Twist

Brilliant or Baloney?

1. Baloney! It's on pages 20-21.
2. Baloney! It's a fantasy novel.
3. Brilliant!
4. Baloney! It's written in prose.
5. Brilliant!

Blighted by Bookworms

A. THE **JUNGLE** BOOK
B. HARRY **POTTER** AND THE PHILOSOPHER'S STONE
C. THE STRANGE CASE OF DOCTOR **JEKYLL** AND MR HYDE
D. A BEAR CALLED **PADDINGTON**
E. THE **CAT** IN THE HAT

Staggering stack

Twenty-seven books

Page 42 Under The Magnifying Glass

The mystery character is Peter Rabbit.

Page 43 Scribbler's Sudoku

Pages 49 It's not rocket science!

1. True
2. True
3. False, they were called *Saturn V* rockets. They were the most powerful ever launched.
4. False, it was a man called Robert Goddard. Stephenson was a steam engineer who is credited with designing a locomotive called the 'Rocket'.
5. False, they are mainly used for delivering satellites into space.
6. True
7. True
8. False, it was taller than a 30-storey building.

Pages 58-59 'S' Spells Solution

					¹Y	O	L	K					
				²S	O	L	D	I	E	R	S		
				³P	A	R	L	I	A	M	E	N	T
⁴W	O	N	D	E	R	L	A	N	D				
					⁵W	I	L	L	I	A	M		
			⁶F	R	A	N	K	E	N	S	T	E	I	N
					⁷G	R	O	W	U	P			
			⁸W	A	T	S	O	N					
		⁹S	L	I	P	P	E	R					
	¹⁰N	A	N	C	Y								

1. The golden inside of HUMPTY DUMPTY. (Pages 10–11)
2. The brave patients of FLORENCE NIGHTINGALE. (Pages 16-17)
3. The houses that treasonous GUY FAWKES had in his sights. (Pages 20-21)
4. The curious place that ALICE discovers down a rabbit hole. (Pages 24-25)
5. The first name of the playwright that penned the tragic tale of HAMLET. (Pages 28-29)
6. The doctor who built the terrible MONSTER with a bolt through its neck. (pages 36-37).
7. The one thing that PETER PAN doesn't want to do. (Pages 40-41)
8. SHERLOCK HOLMES's very loyal assistant. (Pages 38-39)
9. The elegant glass object that fits CINDERELLA a treat. (Pages 50-51)
10. A true friend to poor little OLIVER TWIST. (Pages 56-57)

It's . . . **ODLAW!**

'Thank you for helping Wally and I find the enchanted scroll!

Why not try reading some of the books you've discovered in this Annual?'

Wizard Whitebeard

THE MAN IN THE IRON MASK

GREAT SCIENTISTS

CINDERELLA

FAIRY TALES

THE INVISIBLE MAN

PETER PAN

SPORTS & GAMES

Did you spot?

A bearskin hat
A bowler hat
A chef's hat
A drummer's hat
A sombrero

THE ROMANS

PINOCCHIO

THE WIZARD OF OZ

THE WILD WEST

COOKERY CLASSICS

ALICE IN WONDERLAND

MY BOOK OF BALLET